Here comes Mr. Sillypants.
He has just signed up for swimming lessons.

What if all the other people in the class are better than I am?

I think I'll have a sandwich. Let's see . . . tomatoes, lettuce, olives, cheese,

pickles, tuna, peanut butter, mayonnaise, salami, cheese, pickles, olives, lettuce, and mustard.

A perfect sandwich.

What a nice dream!
I must be on the desert.
The sand is really hot on my feet
and I'm **very** thirsty.

Something tells me
to go this way.

And it was.